Noise

A constant flow of data that provides no information, or obstructs the information.

Noise Amplifier is a process where the government, the market, businesses, or individuals mistakenly take small fluctuations of data and turns them into harmful volatility.

Noise can refer to any random fluctuations of data that hinder the perception of a signal/information.

Our financial markets have been broken for a long time. They are less a catalyst for growth than a drag on the economy.

There is an inherent and invisible flaw in the way our financial system operates.

Instead of sifting the signal from the noise, the markets amplify and increase the noise.

This flaw carries a high price. On an individual level, it promotes the misallocation of savings and investments and compromises economic prosperity. On the company level, organizations spend more resources protecting themselves from the higher level of volatility. The result is a paradox: a thriving financial sector coupled with moderate economic growth.

THE NOISE FACTOR is a financial fantasy that transports the reader to an alternative reality. The book reveals the fundamental principles required to turn off our economy's noise amplifiers and create more productive financial markets.

THE NOISE FACTOR

Hidden Forces that Imperil Financial Markets

Yishai Ashlag
with Meirav Moran

THE NOISE FACTOR
Hidden Forces that Imperil Financial Markets
Yishai Ashlag with Meirav Moran

Additional copies can be obtained from your local bookstore or the publisher:

The North River Press Publishing Corporation
P.O. Box 567
Great Barrington, MA (800) 486-2665
www.northriverpress.com

ISBN: 978-088427-296-0

Printed in Tel Aviv, Israel

Graphic Design Studio Roniverony
Illustrations Ovadia Benishu
Editor Gai Ad
Linguistic editor Rachel Abramowitz

Table of Contents

Prologue

"You'll have to invest all your capital," said the Finance Minister.

"All my capital?" Spivak asked. "Why?"

"That's how we do it here. All your capital, or at least the better part of it."

"I don't see why that's necessary," Spivak said, forcing a smile.

"Gentlemen, we don't have time to argue over it now," The Prime Minister cut in. "This is a state of emergency."

Chapter 1

Eagles Don't Hunt Flies

Dr. Spivak was blinded by a yellow glare as the plane descended. He gazed in wonder at the bright golden fields surrounding the runway, where the wheels of the plane had just touched down.

A long line of brand new ivory-colored cabs waited outside the terminal, each with a golden sunflower on the grille. An official car pulled out from behind them and stopped in front of Spivak, its engine humming quietly. The door opened and a young woman stepped out.

"How do you do, sir," she said with a slight bow of her head. "I'm your driver." She grabbed his suitcase and tossed it into the trunk of the car. Her short, gleaming black hair was skillfully styled, and her green eyes narrowed into thin slits when she smiled. As Spivak slid into the backseat, the driver turned to him and said, "Welcome to our country, sir. You've had a long flight, but don't worry, it isn't far to the city. You'll be able to get some rest very soon."

The driver placed her hands on the steering wheel with the image of a sunflower in the middle, continuing to survey Spivak through the rearview mirror. She was slight, and Spivak wondered how she had lifted his bag with such ease. He showed her the card with the name of his hotel. Naturally, having arrived in a country he'd never visited before, the address didn't mean anything to him. But the driver smiled at him in the rearview mirror. "Your hotel's in a great location," she said. "Next to the park and close to everything. I'm sure they've booked you a room with a lake view."

On the way to the hotel, she told him that the

sunflower represented graciousness and diligence, which is why they had chosen it as their national symbol. In addition to its golden petals, she explained, the flower stored energy for future use, adapted easily to changing conditions, and required little attention to thrive. "All it needs is the farmer's love and it grows on its own," she said. In a few days, Spivak would learn that the sunflowers here also had other qualities he had never imagined.

As they left the broad valley in which the airport was situated, he saw the glowing skyline of the city up ahead. Spivak closed his eyes.

They drove down a long boulevard. The lights in the shop windows had come on, bringing to life the fashionable merchandise on display. Finally, the driver pulled up in front of a modern glass and steel building.

"We're here," she announced. Spivak thanked her, handed her a large tip, and climbed out. A bellboy waiting on the green marble steps came toward them. The driver waited for him to get the suitcase out of the trunk. "There's a beautiful view from here, even at night," she said, before taking off without looking back. Spivak watched as she drove away, the car passing a group of soldiers approaching the hotel. He followed the bellboy into the lobby. When the reception clerk handed him his key, he noticed that the soldiers were now in the bar drinking wine and carrying on a lively conversation.

He had been invited here in the usual way. This invitation was no different from those he regularly received from bank governors, government ministers, and heads of state, as well as individuals aspiring to those positions in the future. They needed advice, so they turned to the "financial wizard" to "point them in the right direction." "It will be of mutual benefit," they invariably noted, hinting at the generous compensation he would be offered, compensation that was not only immediate, but often continued to pay off for a long time to come, thanks to the valuable connections he made on his trips.

He had recognized the same veiled cry for help in the letter from this country. It invited the noted economist to honor them by speaking before parliament on the occasion of their fortieth anniversary celebrations, and by the way, could he please make time to discuss a small but urgent matter. Spivak wondered what could have gone wrong in a country that, in spite of being relatively small and never in the news, was known for its continuing prosperity, was free of poverty, and had enjoyed a high standard of living for so many years. But experience had taught him that even flourishing economies don't call on eagles to hunt flies.

Chapter 2

The Odd Clock

He was free the next morning, before he was scheduled to meet with his hosts. His first meeting in any new country was predictable: an extravagant display of financial power, the hosts singing the praises of their economy. This time, however, he was curious to hear what they had to say. If the rumors and the bits and pieces of data he'd managed to uncover were correct, he could stand to make a tidy profit from the unique industry they had developed. In fact, after receiving their unexpected invitation, he'd increased his investments in companies at home that could benefit from the local technology.

Spivak decided to use his free time to form his own impression of the country, without the usual pomp. It was a lovely day. He went out and strolled down the broad boulevard in the direction of the stock exchange. The city had long ago woken up to another routine weekday. The café tables on the sidewalk were full, and the shops he'd passed the night before were bustling with customers. He reached the end of the boulevard and stopped in front of an imposing building with steps on either side leading up to the entrance. Above the grand columns was an inscription that began with the word "Here." Although the sunlight reflecting off the gold letters made it impossible for him to read the rest, he assumed he was in the right place. He climbed the wide steps and arrived at an ornate door adorned with gold carvings. Turning around, he could see the tops of the trees on the boulevard. Trading must be in full swing by now, he thought, pushing on the door, which gave way easily. Once inside, he heard a ringing voice call out from somewhere in the cool space, "Good morning. Welcome."

Coming toward him was a tall man with an athletic build, dressed in a fine suit that was not at all in keeping with the noisy rattle of the heavy key chain in his hand. "Ah, Dr. Spivak! I would recognize you anywhere. Welcome! It is an honor," the man said. Hanging the keys on his belt, he shook Spivak's hand warmly. "It's a long flight, I know. Unfortunately, trading is closed at the moment. Can you come back tomorrow?"

"The market is closed today?" Spivak asked in surprise.

"Oh, no. But look at the time," the man said, pointing to the wall behind him, on which a strange clock hung. The hands were moving at the usual pace, but only two numbers, ten and eleven, were indicated. Spivak glanced at his watch. "It's eleven o'clock. When will trading be resumed?"

"Tomorrow at ten."

"Tomorrow? So what will you do later today when the latest news comes in?"

"To tell the truth, nothing usually happens here after eleven."

"But things happen before ten?" asked Spivak, chuckling.

"Actually, not a lot happens before ten either. To be honest, nothing much happens here at all, and certainly not every day or even every week."

"Okay, thank you," Spivak said, turning to leave. "I'll try to come some other time."

"You're welcome to come any day, before eleven," the man called to him, his keys rattling.

Spivak stopped in his tracks. "Trading is halted every day at eleven?" he asked.

"Yes. It opens every day at ten and closes at eleven. So far, we haven't needed more than an hour a day."

"Isn't that a shame in an economy like yours? You're missing out on so many opportunities to buy and sell."

"True. I used to say the same thing," the man said, glancing at the clock on the wall. "But what do you actually gain from more buying and selling?"

"The more a stock is traded, the more people want to buy it and sell it," Spivak answered, patiently explaining the obvious. "When the stock exchange is open all day, buyers know they'll be able to sell their shares anytime they want."

"But people don't want to sell their shares at any time. They want to wait for the company to make a profit."

"Trading doesn't really affect a company's profits. But just think about the stocks themselves!" Spivak said with a smile. "When investors know they can sell their stock at any given moment in the future, the more people want to buy in the present, and so the price of the stock goes up."

The tall man creased his brow, considering, and then said, "It seems to me that if the price of the stock goes up but the company's profit doesn't, the investor might be disappointed."

"That's the whole trick," Spivak said with a mischievous grin. "As soon as the investor starts to worry that he might be disappointed, he can instantly sell his shares to someone else. Think about it," he said as he turned to leave.

Chapter 3

Starting Out

A large black van stopped in front of the hotel. The driver who had picked him up at the airport stepped out. "Good morning," she said, opening the passenger door to reveal, to Spivak's surprise, a well-appointed conference room: comfortable high-back chairs with fold out tables of shiny metal. The Finance Minister was waiting inside. He rose, shook Spivak's hand, and gestured to the chair opposite him. "Welcome. I hope you feel rested. We have a long ride ahead of us."

The van pulled out. They rode in silence for a while, and then the Minister pulled a file from the briefcase beside him. "When we get to the plant, the engineers will give us a tour of the production lines. We've gotten the latest figures together for you, as you requested, so you can prepare for your talk before parliament," he said, handing the file to Spivak.

They were heading west. Sunflower fields lined both sides of the road. On the left were the familiar yellow sunflowers Spivak had seen around the airport when he arrived. On the right were rows upon rows of pink sunflowers. Seeing the amazement on Spivak's face, the Minister explained proudly that the yellow flowers were used to make energy-producing biological batteries, while the pink ones served as the raw material for a whole range of other products. "They're like your plastic," he said. "but with one difference. Here, when pink sunflower products are thrown out, they're ground up and used as fertilizer for agricultural purposes. The sunflower plant purchases most of the pink waste. We try to recycle without the need for more energy."

After a few more miles, the Minister opened a hidden drawer and took out a bowl of assorted sunflower seeds along with a small bottle of some kind of liquid. "Try this," he said, pouring them each a glass of the liquid. "It's excellent. Another product we've developed from sunflowers." He emptied his glass in a single gulp. Spivak sipped at his gingerly. To his surprise, it was very good. It had a strong alcoholic kick, but there was a delicate sweetness underneath. He wouldn't give up good champagne for it, but it definitely increased his interest in the profitable business opportunity that seemed to be beckoning him from the fields of flowers. They reached the plant and climbed out of the van. A group of scientists was waiting to greet them.

In a few minutes, the official visit to the main sunflower plant would begin, and Spivak would learn that the Finance Minister had a Ph.D. in botany and was the founder of the sunflower company, the flagship of the local economy, as well as its first chairman. He would also learn that the tour and the warm welcome he was being given were the first steps in an attempt to neutralize the threat that was casting a dark shadow over the country and its citizens: the neighboring land had set its sights on their sunflower fields and was moving troops to the border.

That was the reason that more soldiers were seen in the city streets every day, the reason the Finance Minister had suddenly started drinking before noon, and the reason the Prime Minister couldn't sleep at night. The threat, and the defense strategy they had devised, known by those privy to the secret as "The Plan," were also the real reason for Spivak's invitation to this prosperous country.

Chapter 4

The Purple Sunflower

The CEO of the sunflower company was waiting for Spivak and the Finance Minister at the entrance to the plant. Beside him stood a tall slender man who was introduced to Spivak as the major investor in the company. Lean and lithe, the man reminded Spivak of a greyhound he had had as a child. After the official welcoming ceremony, they entered the large laboratory facilities, where dozens of scientists were at work. From there they went on to the long, narrow production floor. Gleaming metal drums of different sizes were scattered about under a high glass ceiling. As they walked the length of the hall, between the drums and the brightly colored machines emitting a gentle clicking sound, the engineers described the production process for each of the plant's products.

When they reached the wide opening at the end of the hall, the engineers and scientists stayed behind and the four men walked out into the sunflower fields. The Finance Minister and tall investor led the way down a broad furrow, with Spivak and the CEO following, walking side by side. As Spivak trod along the track, the clods under his feet broke into fine pink grains. They reached a glass building in the middle of the field. The CEO placed his hand on the transparent wall and it slid open. They went inside, and the wall closed behind them.

"Very nice," the Finance Minister exclaimed at the sight of rows of tiny neon purple sunflowers. "I'm glad to see you're moving forward as planned." The CEO bent down and fingered the glowing petals.

"This is our little secret," he said to Spivak with a bright smile, his eyes gleaming. He stole a glance at the silent investor, who was looking at the flowers with obvious discomfort. "Tell the truth, you wouldn't believe it if you didn't see it with your own eyes, right? Luckily, our Finance Minister knows what you can get from flowers if you give them the proper attention, and what protection they can offer investors." Placing his hand on the CEO's shoulder, the Finance Minister said drily, "What's lucky is that Dr. Spivak is here. If all goes well, we won't have to use the purple sunflower."

They exited the secret greenhouse and made their way to a bower at the edge of the field, where a hostess was waiting with cold drinks. "I have to admit I had my doubts about your visit here," the CEO said to Spivak. "I didn't think you'd be interested in our business."

"I admit," Spivak replied warmly, "I didn't think an agricultural venture could be so interesting." Turning to the investor, he added, "It's been fascinating." He raised the glass in his hand. "A business like yours should be in the headlines. It's a shame to hide it away in a stock exchange that's only open for an hour a day."

"We don't hide it at all," said the CEO, clinking glasses with Spivak as his eyes darted back and forth between the Finance Minister and the investor. "We've heard about the long hours of trade in your stock exchange. We believe..."

"My dear friends," the Finance Minister broke in, raising his glass and tapping it to get their attention. "I want to thank you for your warm welcome and the excellent tour of your facilities." After they all joined in the toast, he shook hands with the CEO and the major investor, and led Spivak back to the van. The driver hurried to open the door for them.

Chapter 5

Darkness On The Horizon

As they drove back to the city, the Finance Minister stared at the open road ahead in silence. Spivak wondered when his host would feel the time was right to reveal the real reason he had been invited here. When quite some time had passed and the Minister still hadn't said a word, he decided to start the conversation himself. "Your sunflower business is even more impressive than I imagined from the figures you gave me this morning," he said. No reply. A few minutes later, the Finance Minister leaned forward and tapped on the window separating them from the driver. It seemed to be some sort of signal. The driver raised her eyes to the rearview mirror and nodded. The Finance Minister leaned back in his seat. "Wait, there's more to see," he said, returning his eyes to the road. He had a straight back and thick white hair combed back to reveal a smooth tanned forehead. Although he was over seventy, his movements were agile and his posture erect. Contrary to expectations from a senior public official, he was wearing neither a suit nor a tie. Instead, he was dressed in a spotless white shirt tucked into dark blue, impeccably pressed pants. Nevertheless, he didn't appear at all concerned by the dirt on his expensive leather shoes from their walk through the fields.

They turned off the highway. The driver skillfully steered the van up a narrow winding track that climbed a tree-studded hill. When they reached the top, she drove along the ridge until the track widened a little, stopping at the edge of a large clearing. She got out to open the door, but the

Finance Minister didn't wait. He pulled it open himself and the driver got back behind the wheel. Spivak followed his host out of the van. It was already dark out, and the air was clear and cool. The Minister led the way to a marble-paved lookout point. The two men gazed at the brightly lit landscape spreading out below.

"Take a look at this valley," the Minister said, gesturing broadly. "The lights never go out here. Dozens of enterprises in every possible branch of industry. Take your pick. Over there on the right, at one o'clock, they're doing agricultural research, developing plants that can grow in extreme climates. At three o'clock there are agrifood factories producing foodstuffs that stay fresh for quite a long time without the need for artificial preservatives. Just below us, at six o'clock, are laboratories creating raw materials for industrial production that are strong and durable, and break down by themselves without causing pollution. On the left, between nine and ten o'clock, they're developing electronic components that use energy almost without emitting heat. The R&D departments of the firms in the valley never close, not even for a day."Spivak noticed a black hole in the landscape, on the horizon. "What's over there, at twelve o'clock?" he asked. The Finance Minister seemed to have been expecting the question. "That's our largest army base," he answered without hesitation. He took a few steps forward to the edge of the platform, making sure that Spivak was following. Pointing to the darkness straight ahead, he said, "Those are the gates to the base. Most of it extends across the hills on the other side of the valley. It controls all the territory there, up to the border. The country across the border is hostile. They want to take over our sunflower fields, the ones you saw earlier." The Minister looked directly at Spivak. "The last time our army went into battle was one hundred and eighty years ago. I don't know if it's capable of defending us today, and no one will assure me that it is." He wiped his brow, looked toward the horizon again, and then returned his eyes to Spivak. "Everyone is in agreement that we have to sign a defense alliance with your country as soon as possible. A defense alliance that would ensure your country has a significant economic interest in our country and, therefore, would be willing to protect it. The alliance is the only way out of the war. We're even willing to sell the sunflower company to achieve our goal. Otherwise, we'll be forced to use the purple sunflower."

Chapter 6
Looking For Headlines

It was only when Spivak got back to the hotel that he had a chance to check his phone. While he was looking through the messages, he got a call from the Governor of the Central Bank at home. In the background, he could hear the familiar screeching sound of the hawk the Governor referred to as his good-luck charm.

"Did you forget what day it is?" The Governor had

to shout to be heard over the noise of the bird that had lived in his office for years. "I give my report on the state of the economy tomorrow. We're in pretty good shape, but afterwards I'll have to deal with the press. All they want is headlines, and you always come up with ideas."

Spivak smiled. "You called at a good time. I've got a great headline for you. And I'm not going to deny it will also promote my own interests. Today I learned the secret of success in this country. They've found a way to create energy on a large scale from sunflowers. They're almost at the stage where they can export the technology and reduce the world's demand for oil."

"We'd certainly benefit from a drop in oil prices. And you don't have to tell me how much the oil-guzzling companies you bought up recently would profit," the Governor said. "I'd be delighted to be able to tell the press that the cost of energy isn't going to rise thanks to flowers. Come on, Spivak, give me something serious."

"You can be as skeptical as you like, sir, but my investors want to see results. I'm convinced the price of oil is going to drop. There's the potential for a huge deal here, and I'm not going to miss out on it." The roar of an approaching fighter plane filled Spivak's room. There was no need to concern the Governor with threats of war, Spivak thought, hurrying to close the window. "They didn't invite me here to give a speech. They want to do business with us."

"I don't get you, Spivak. You almost died laughing when you told me their stock exchange is closed for most of the day. What kind of business can you possibly do with those people?"

"They gave me a tour of their sunflower plant today and offered to sell it to me," Spivak said. "They're clueless. They even introduced me to the Major Shareholder. I told the Finance Minister the company was very impressive. Then I explained that it would be much simpler to list it on our stock exchange. He hadn't even thought of that. I wish you'd seen how enthusiastic he was when he grasped what I was proposing. Look, they don't understand the first thing about capital markets, but their industry is world-class. You can just imagine how high it can go on our market. I'll work out the details of the stock flotation tomorrow. Do whatever you like with the information."

Chapter 7

Chance Encounters By The Lake

The driver came to the lake every day, sometimes twice a day. She came at different times and in different clothes so as not to attract attention. The swan in the lake knew her well, however. Whenever it saw her coming, it paddled to the shore, knowing she would feed it sunflower seeds.

Spivak was strolling along the stone walkway, its pavers turning red in the setting sun, when he caught sight of the driver on a lacquered oak bench, bent over a thick blue notebook in her lap.

"Good evening," Spivak greeted her. "What a lucky coincidence."

She raised her eyes. "Good evening, Dr. Spivak," she answered, clutching the notebook to her chest.

"Do you write poetry?" he asked, pointing to the notebook.

She smiled at him shyly, lowered her eyes, and slid over to make room for him on the bench. "I wanted to tell you who I am and what I do on the way to your hotel, but you looked exhausted after your flight," she said. "I want to be an actress. I'm saving up for acting classes, and driving pays well." All of a sudden she rose and walked toward a man in a suit standing at the edge of the lake under a tree whose branches hung over the water. They exchanged a few words. She opened her notebook and wrote something in it. After another short exchange, the man walked away and she came back to the bench and sat down next to Spivak.

"That man didn't look like he was in show business," Spivak said.

She threw her head back and laughed. "You're

right. I also do business with people like him." Again, she rose and headed toward another man in a suit who was approaching the lake on the path Spivak had taken. They spoke, she wrote something in her notebook, and the suit turned around and went back the way he had come.

The swan kept a close eye on her. So did Spivak. As she talked to her clients, she leaned forward without letting go of the blue notebook, brushing a leaf off the toe of her shoe. She came back and sat down beside him again.

"How is the theater scene around here? Any shows you can recommend?" Spivak asked.

"I'll think of something. The theater here is excellent. Better than the stock exchange," she said, as if sharing a secret, while her eyes surveyed the park.

A woman was approaching from the other side of the lake. She moved lightly, carrying a violin in her hand.

As soon as she saw the violinist, the driver quickly tucked the notebook into her shoulder bag and stood up. "I have to go," she said. "Now you know where to find me. Maybe we can go to a show tomorrow," she called before disappearing up the path.

Spivak was still trying to recover from her abrupt departure when the violinist stopped beside him. "I didn't know you were interested in the theater, Dr. Spivak," she said.

"Excuse me, madam. Have we met?"

"Everyone knows who you are, Dr. Spivak."

That's strange, he thought. The violinist sat down on the bench and said softly, "If you're counting on connections with our economic leaders, it would be a good idea for you to meet with someone who can really help you."

The swan was still watching them. Suddenly, it flapped its wings and poke his head down into the dark water.

Chapter 8

The Finance Minister's Bag Of Apples

The next morning, the Finance Minister accompanied Spivak to a meeting with the chairman of the stock exchange. They entered the stately building, climbed a broad flight of stairs, and crossed long silent corridors until they reached an impressive door. The Minister gestured for Spivak to wait and knocked on the door. Hearing no response, he cracked it open and stuck his head in, and then motioned for Spivak to follow him in.

Beyond the door was a spacious hall with a white marble floor and huge windows flooding the room with natural light. At the far end was a wide desk in front of a ceiling-high bookcase. "Good morning, Mr. Chairman," the Minister said, his voice echoing in the large space. From behind the desk, an imposing figure rose to greet them. "Welcome. I'm so glad you're here. Make yourselves at home." To Spivak's surprise, the same tall man he had met here on his first day in the country was striding toward them. "Nice to see you again, Doctor," he said warmly, shaking Spivak's hand.

The Chairman led them to a comfortable seating area in a corner of the room. A pot of tea was waiting on the table. As they settled themselves, he poured them each a cup. "What do you think of our stock exchange?" he asked. Spivak took a sip of tea and cleared his throat. "I...eh...it's very interesting," he answered.

"We used to have a large staff working long hours," their host said. "There's no reason to be here after eleven these days, but we're still in the same building. Where else would you find such wonderful architecture? And it reminds us of the past. We don't want to forget it."

Spivak leaned back in his chair. It was clear to him that the local stock market needed a good shaking up. "You have great opportunities here. You can make a lot of money," he said. "All you have to do is rake it in. Your economy is thriving, your companies are profitable, and that's an excellent starting point. But you're not taking advantage of it. It hurts me to see it."

After the visit to the sunflower plant, the Finance Minister had explained their need for a defense alliance with his country. He was now looking at Spivak expectantly. "The first step," Spivak explained, "is to list the sunflower company on our stock exchange. That will light a spark. The demand will encourage other firms to do the same, and from there, things will start to take off."

"I think that's an excellent idea," the Chairman said, glancing at the Finance Minister before going on. "But I'm sure you remember that trade opens here at ten and closes an hour later, at eleven."

"That's okay," Spivak said. He didn't need the Chairman to spell it out for him. The empty corridors in the seemingly abandoned building made the picture very clear. "It's a big world, but nevertheless we conduct global trade. Everyone buys and sells everyone else's commodities." He saw the Chairman's face break into a smile. "It's the same with the stock exchange. When the market opens in one part of the world, the traders on the other side of the world are asleep. It's only natural. You just sleep for longer than most. The time difference even has its advantages. Trust me, it's no problem," he said, his voice rising as he grew more excited. "On the contrary, it's an opportunity."

"Yes, it's an opportunity for all of us," the Chairman said, refilling their cups and gently pushing a plate of cookies toward the Minister."I have no doubt, Dr. Spivak, that you can find an advantage even in our unusual manner of trade. Something that will only allow the price of the stock to change by ten percent or more."

"Ten percent?" Spivak asked, astounded. The Finance Minister hadn't mentioned that.

"Yes. We don't quote smaller changes," the Chairman said proudly.

Spivak swallowed uneasily. "How can you make

a profit that way? But even a two-percent change represents considerable gain. Even from a change of one percent you can turn a large profit."

"Yes, of course! But we stopped quoting those fluctuations a long time ago," the Chairman answered.

Spivak's eyes passed between the Finance Minister, hunkered down in his chair, and the buoyant Chairman. He was finding it hard to believe that the man speaking with such pride of choking the life out of trading was the Chairman of the stock exchange. Spivak might be a financial wizard, but he'd never claimed to be able to raise the dead. "If you agree that one percent, or even a quarter of one percent, can represent a lot of money, why don't you quote those fluctuations in stock prices?" he asked.

The Chairman turned toward his desk and the bookcase behind it. "We don't quote them because we only quote changes. Until forty years ago, we operated the same way you do. But then we decided to stop quoting non-changes, and we continue to follow that policy."

"I don't understand," Spivak said. "You said you

quote fluctuations of ten percent." By now he was utterly confused.

"We only quote changes of ten percent or more. Anything less and there's no way of knowing if it reflects a real change. So we don't quote it."

Spivak tried a different tack. "No problem. We'll help you," he said. "Our exchange estimates the price of thousands of stocks every day, all day long. It won't be hard for your traders to learn to use the mechanisms for calculating fluctuations to the fraction of a percent and issuing stock quotes for every company listed on the exchange in real time. If you like, I can..."

"Pardon me, Dr. Spivak," the Finance Minister cut in. "I don't know what your mechanisms calculate. We're interested in listing our sunflower company on your stock exchange, as you propose, but the value of a company can't be measured in fractions of a percent. A company isn't a bag of apples. When I go to the grocer, he puts the bag on a scale. If I replace a small apple with a large one and it weighs three percent more, I pay more. If I replace a large one with a small one and it weighs half a percent less, I pay less. You can measure height, distance, or temperature in fractions of a percent because they're all physical entities, like apples. But a company is like an apple orchard whose value is assessed by the size of the crop it yields. One year there's a bumper crop and the next year there isn't. And then the third year the orchard yields twice as many apples, but the consumers' taste in fruit has changed and suddenly they prefer pears. How can you calculate the value of the orchard to a precise fraction of a percent?" The Minister took another cookie and devoured it in one bite. Then he leaned back and gazed at Spivak, waiting for an answer.

An academic discussion with the Minister wouldn't get Spivak anywhere. The sunflower company was worth billions. If he could bring it back with him, the traders would jump on it. And the longer the sunflowers were in the headlines, the lower the price of oil would fall and the more Spivak would make. But the botany-loving Minister was wasting their time with financial analogies of the agricultural kind, ignoring the urgent issues before them. Their stock exchange was stagnant, their economy was run by farmers, and back home they were burning money. "Gentlemen," he said, "I'm merely trying to demonstrate how a modern stock exchange works. In order for a capital market to thrive, every fluctuation in stock prices, no matter how small, must be quoted."

"Dr. Spivak is right, Mr. Minister. Before the Big Crash, we also quoted every fluctuation. There was even a time when a non-change was considered a change and we quoted that too," the Chairman said. Spivak could hear the excitement in his voice.

"How do you know that what you quote today is a change and not a non-change?" Spivak asked.

"It's very simple," the Chairman answered, smiling. "I already told you. A change can only be a difference of ten percent or more."

"So what's a non-change?"

"Well, it's...everything else," the Chairman answered, glancing at the Minister. "Everything else is just random fluctuations in the existing situation."

"And when you quote a ten-percent change you're sure it's not just a random fluctuation? The value of the company has really changed by precisely ten percent?"

"I'm quite sure that a ten-percent change is a real change, and obviously it isn't precisely ten percent," said the Chairman. "But it's also obvious that a fluctuation of a quarter of a percent is a non-change. That's why we don't quote it. To be honest, sometimes I wonder what it feels like to quote non-changes," he said, adding wistfully, "Once upon a time they must have had fun around here."

The Chairman's interest in stock trading ignited a spark of hope in Spivak. He rose and declared, "Gentlemen, we can resurrect those exciting times in your stock exchange. We can rejuvenate stocks that have long been forgotten and we can bring the traders back to the market. A system that reports every fluctuation in price in real time will once again bring glory to this great institution. When you've got solid companies and lively trading, the sky's the limit. And you already have plenty of great companies. Let's get started."

"Hold on a minute, Dr. Spivak," the Finance Minister said. "We all want to move forward. But we will never quote non-changes. A company isn't a bag of apples."

Spivak remained standing. "Quite right, sir. Nobody thinks the value of a company actually changes by the fractions of a percent that govern stock transactions. Trade can't represent the precise value of a company at any given moment. As you say, it's not a bag of apples. But you have to remember that we're not buying fruit at the grocery store. We're talking about the sunflower company, and the urgent issues it can impact. You present your excellent financial reports, including new developments, and our analysts will do the market research and publish optimistic forecasts in the business press. The journalists will pounce on it. Every article, every report, every transaction will influence the stock price. Even if the change is only half a percent up or down, what difference does it make? In terms of sunflowers, it represents billions. We'll all come out ahead. You'll get your defense alliance and we'll make money."

"The sunflower company is one of our strongest holdings," the Chairman said tentatively.

"It would be a shame not to leverage its success for the defense alliance you need," Spivak said.

"That's what we're trying to do," said the Finance Minister. He seemed relieved that Spivak had returned to the primary reason for his visit. "We all understand that this is a once-in-a-lifetime opportunity. But I'm sure you can find a way to list the company on your stock exchange without quoting non-changes. You have to agree, Dr. Spivak, what can't be measured can't be measured."

Spivak was losing patience. His hope of breathing life into the corpse the two men insisted on calling their "stock exchange" was beginning to waver. And he was no longer confident that he would leave the country having struck a deal. He almost walked out, but he needed those sunflowers. They could do wonders for his bottom line. Breathing a deep sigh, he tried again. "Gentlemen, stock prices always change by fractions of a percent. A little higher, a little lower. Transactions are concluded throughout the day at prices agreed upon by both sides. Prices are quoted in real time. Everyone can see them, and everyone buys and sells. What's the problem?"

"Yes, Mr. Minister," the Chairman agreed, apparently won over by Spivak. "We've always said that non-changes are random fluctuations in the existing situation. All we have to do is quote them, as Dr. Spivak says. I can do that. I have the time."

"Wonderful. We'll help you," said Spivak. Turning

to the Finance Minister, he added, "You'll see, Mr. Minister, the more transactions there are, the more closely the price will represent the real value of the company."

"No, no, Dr. Spivak. I'm afraid you're wrong again," the Minister said. "It's quite the opposite. Quoting minute changes in the stock price dissociates it even more from the true value of the company. It doesn't promote precision, it detracts from it."

"A precise quote detracts from precision?" Spivak asked in a querulous tone. He wondered what other surprises the Finance Minister had in store for him.

"Precisely. A precise quote detracts from precision," the Chairman echoed.

Only God can help someone who believes that precision detracts from precision, Spivak thought to himself, sitting down again. I may be a superstar, but I'm not God.

The large windows started to shake as a fighter plane passed overhead. The noise reminded the Finance Minister of the reason they were having this discussion. He slid another cookie into his mouth and gestured for the Chairman to pour Spivak more tea.

"I've noticed how much self-discipline you have," he said to Spivak. "You haven't touched the cookies. How often do you weigh yourself?"

"Usually once a week."

"Why not once a day, or three times a day?" the Minister challenged.

"That's all I need," Spivak laughed. "I know myself. If I saw I'd put on three ounces I'd be outside doing laps around the park in a second."

"I'm just the same," the Minister said, smiling. "When the scale tells me I've lost a pound, I allow myself two helpings of dessert at dinner."

"And then you weigh yourself and discover you've put on two pounds," Spivak joked, glad that the mood in the room was lighter.

"Precisely. Then what's the meaning of a change of three ounces in body weight?" the Minister asked.

"It's a non-change," the Chairman cut in, jumping up.

"Right, just a random fluctuation in the existing situation. So is there any point in weighing yourself every hour?" the Minister went on.

"No," said the Chairman. "Changes from one

hour to the next don't prove anything. Frequent measurements of insignificant changes are simply confusing and stressful. Random fluctuations are nothing but noise, and when you respond to noise, it gets louder. If we keep getting on the scale and measuring the change in our weight in ounces, we'll eat more than we should, or exercise excessively, or fast and then overeat again. And it will be very hard to keep track of our true weight."

"Correct!" the Finance Minister said approvingly.

Spivak sighed. "Mr. Minister," he said, "I want to make one thing clear. If we don't quote the small changes in stock prices, people will lose interest in trading shares and we can close the stock exchange."

"We don't trade in shares here," the Chairman proclaimed. Quoting the gold inscription on the front of the building, he added, "Here we invest in businesses." The Finance Minister nodded in agreement.

Another plane thundered across the sky.

"Exactly right. So we only quote changes when they are signs that something new has actually happened," he said firmly. "Small fluctuations stem from events that are only marginally related to the state of the company at best, or worse, they're merely arbitrary. Most commonly, they are responses to meaningless reports. They reflect one trader's expectations regarding another trader's predictions of a third trader's attitude to a change in the stock price, which itself was no more than a response to a meaningless report in the first place. This leads to larger and more misleading fluctuations. The price of the stock can soar as a result of a series of small increases, each fueling the next, without any connection to the value of the company. Or else the price might drop and then might rise again. All this activity causes serious damage, because the true state of the company is forgotten in the commotion of trade. When there's an indication of a real change that requires immediate intervention, it goes unnoticed amid all the noise. Attention is focused on managing the stock instead of on managing the company." He gestured with his hand and the Chairman rose and went back to the bookshelf behind his desk.

"Look, Dr. Spivak," the Finance Minister said in a low voice, "I brought you here because you suggested listing the sunflower company on your stock exchange and you convinced me it was a simple way to implement The Plan and ensure we get the defense alliance we need. The Prime Minister agreed. But we will not allow small fluctuations in the company's stock price to be quoted. They may be very small, but the risk of quoting them is very big."

Yet another plane roared overhead. "Sometimes you don't have any choice," Spivak said. "Times change, and you have to adapt to new circumstances."

The Chairman returned with a little book in his hand. "Forty years ago, when a company's profits changed by ten percent, the stock price changed by thirty percent. It happened over and over again, with every company," he said dramatically, handing Spivak the book. Its white cover bore a single word in gold letters: "Quiet." "This is for you, from the special fortieth anniversary edition."

"Thank you," said Spivak as the Chairman

resumed his seat next to the Finance Minister. No one said a word. The silence isn't helping anyone, thought Spivak. This wasn't the way he'd expected the meeting to end.

Finally the Finance Minister spoke. "We have a good reason for sticking to our position," he said. "Investors buy and sell shares according to a clock that measures time in years. If we encourage the kind of trade you suggest, if we start using a clock that measures time in hours, minutes, and seconds, the profits from trading stocks will be greater than the profits from investments. The investors will prefer to be traders and get instant gratification. Instead of working to improve the company's business, they'll only work to increase their profit from the stock market. That will be very damaging not only for the sunflower company, but for the whole of the industry in our country."

It was clear to Spivak that the road he had plotted was blocked, but then he thought of a different route they could take. He glanced at his watch. The Finance Minister rose, and Spivak followed him out of the Chairman's office.

"There are other ways to implement The Plan," Spivak said when they were outside. "You can buy a defense pact from us. All you have to do is borrow money from us and pay a high interest on the loan. Given the state of your economy, that shouldn't be a problem. I'm sure the Prime Minister will agree."

Chapter 9

Early Rising

Spivak tossed and turned in the hotel bed. It wasn't the unfamiliar bed itself that kept him awake; he couldn't have asked for a more comfortable mattress. It must be that damned jetlag, he thought. It always seemed to get to him a few days after a long flight. The clock on the bedside table showed just after three in the morning. He tried his best to fall back to sleep. The next time he looked at the clock only fifty minutes had passed. He realized he wasn't going to get any more sleep that night. He got up, switched on the coffee maker, and checked his phone. He was expecting a couple of messages from home, but instead he was inundated by anxious communications from the bankers who had given him business loans and the managers of the companies he had invested their money in. They were all feeling the pressure of the soaring price of oil. The managers were witnessing their profits erode and the bankers, as usual, were worried Spivak wouldn't be able to repay the loans.

Before he left, Spivak had assured everyone that oil prices would drop and their profits would go sky-high. Now they were demanding an explanation. But he wasn't overly concerned. He'd finalize the terms for the defense alliance later today and, like always, the traders would be encouraged by rumors of good news, spread with the aid of the governor of the central bank, and the mood in the market would lighten. He poured himself a cup of coffee and glanced at the messages that were still flooding in. He decided to cancel his breakfast meeting with the Finance Minister. That would give him time for a series of reassuring calls to the nervous bankers and stressed-out company directors. He sent a short apology to the Minister, saying he would meet him at the office of the Governor of the Central Bank in time for their scheduled meeting. There was no need to send a car for him, he added. He'd make his own way there.

The Finance Minister saw Spivak's message immediately. He hadn't gotten much sleep that night either. He'd arrived home very late after meeting with the Prime Minister to get the Minister's approval for another change in The Plan. It wasn't easy. The Prime Minister was adamant that they go back to the original plan: Spivak would buy the sunflower company and intervene on their behalf with his government to secure the defense alliance they so desperately needed. The Finance Minister was compelled to remind the Prime Minister of the current circumstances. "He doesn't want to buy the company," he explained. "That's why we agreed to his proposal to list it on their stock market. But when we met with the

Director of the stock exchange today, he insisted on quoting non-changes in the share price. Of course, I couldn't agree to that, so we had to abandon the idea. Spivak can get us the defense alliance, so we have to give his new proposition a chance. We don't have any choice," he added.

Chapter 10

The Governor's Pie

The concierge at the hotel drew Spivak a map. Following it, Spivak arrived at a nondescript office tower with a restaurant on the street level. A waiter spread white cloths on the tables in preparation for breakfast service. Spivak surveyed the surroundings and saw that all the adjacent buildings looked exactly the same. Afraid the concierge had sent him to the wrong place, he went inside, hoping someone could point him in the right direction. "Excuse me," he said to a man waiting for the elevator, "Do you know where I can find the Central Bank?"

"It's upstairs," the man said, gesturing for him to follow him into the elevator. "Ninth floor. I think it's on the right." Indeed, when he got off on nine, he saw the Finance Minister waiting for him impatiently outside one of the glass doors in the corridor. "Good morning," the Minister said. "Let's go. The Governor is ready for us. We'll settle things here, and then we can move forward." He opened the door and they entered a modest office. A woman was sitting with her back to them, facing a glass wall that looked out on the park below. The Minister cleared his throat and the woman turned around.

"Good morning," she said amiably, settling her arms comfortably on the armrests of her chair. Spivak recognized her immediately: the violinist he had met by the lake. Pointing to the chairs in front of her desk, she said, "Please, take a seat. They'll bring up refreshments in just a minute."

"Allow me to introduce Dr. Spivak," the Finance

Minister said to the Governor when they were seated. "I'm sure you've heard of him."

"Dr. Spivak's name precedes him," said the Governor evenly. The door opened, and the waiter Spivak had seen downstairs entered. He placed a tray of fruit, cheese, and a pitcher of juice on the wide desk. "Help yourselves," the Governor said as she rose. She escorted the young man to the door, slid a coin into his hand, and closed the door behind him.

"I understand you've been informed of the change in The Plan," the Finance Minister said when the Governor had returned to her desk. "We'll be taking out a large loan. We don't need it, but it will get us the defense alliance, and we do need that. We won't have any trouble making the payments on it."

"I spoke with the Prime Minister this morning," said the Governor, pulling out a single sheet of paper. "I told him what you know as well as I do, Mr. Minister. If we borrow money abroad and issue government bonds to be traded on foreign stock exchanges, we'll have to instruct the banks to put a limit on the loans they offer here. They'll have to reduce their customers' line of credit and give lower mortgages to our citizens. Businesses will suffer as well. We won't be able to permit them to issue new company bonds."

"We've already solved that problem," said the Minister. "I thought the Prime Minister brought you up to speed."

The Governor examined a pie chart in front of her on the desk, and then glanced at Spivak. "I guess the Prime Minister didn't have time to fill me in on all the details, so he sent you here to explain how the magic trick works," she said. "How do we cut another slice out of the national debt after we've already divided it up among the banks, the credit companies, and the company bonds traded on the stock exchange? We only have one pie. The only way you can give a slice to an additional customer is to give smaller slices to all the others."

Spivak examined the display of string instruments on the walls. His eye was caught by a large cold hearth with books in identical bindings stacked up beside it. "People complain when their line of credit is reduced and the size of their mortgage is limited," he stated.

"The Plan calls for enlarging the pie," the Finance Minister said to the Governor. "The citizens won't feel the difference. They can go on borrowing money from the banks and credit companies just as they did before, and companies can continue to raise money by selling bonds to the public. Nothing will change." He paused for a moment before adding, "All we have to do is make a bigger pie. We increase the debt, and no one gets hurt."

"I understand," the Governor said, "but we've never increased the debt before. We don't do that. For forty years the national debt has remained a set ratio to the gross domestic product. I don't have to remind you what things were like before that. We let the national debt balloon out of control, and it ended in the Big Crash."

The Finance Minister and the Governor had worked side-by-side for many years, and the Minister often found himself envying his colleague. He'd have loved to work part-time in a building by the lake with swans and to play the violin in the afternoon. He knew the Governor was right, but these were not normal times. Sighing, he placed his hands on her desk and said, "No, you don't have to remind me. We all remember the Big Crash. But even though The Plan requires increasing the debt, and even though we've never done it before, we're going to do it now. We're going to take the loan and pay the interest. That's the price we have to pay for the defense alliance."

"As I'm sure you realize, I am also aware of recent events," the Governor said, her voice trembling. She took a sip of juice and replaced the glass gently on her desk. "If we have to defend ourselves, there are other ways to do it. We have never increased the debt and I'm not convinced that we have to do it now."

Spivak wasn't surprised by the exchange between the Governor, who was no longer smiling, and the anxious Finance Minister. Now it was his turn. He picked up the page with the debt pie chart. "The Minister is right, Madam Governor," he said, "and so are you. It's important to limit the size of the national debt. But I'm sure you'll agree that the ultimate goal isn't to preserve the level of debt, but to protect the country and the economy. That's why we're here. Let's not waste any more time. Let's go over the figures and then we can take it to the Prime Minister."

"What figures do you need?" the Governor asked.

"Unemployment rate, consumer price index, housing starts, retail inventory."

"I'm sorry, Dr. Spivak, I don't have that data," the Governor interrupted. "I don't collect it."

"So who does?" Spivak asked, placing the pie chart back on the desk and turning to the Finance Minister.

"No one. We don't collect that kind of data," the Governor answered for him. "The Central Bank used to be located in a large building opposite the stock exchange. It had a large staff devoted to collecting data, the way you do it in your country. The figures were printed in monthly editions that were distributed to the banks, the insurance companies, the press. I still have a few old copies," she said, pointing to the stack of books in beige bindings beside the hearth.

"We don't need all those figures to increase the size of the debt in order to implement The Plan," the Minister said irritably, pushing the pie chart closer to the Governor. "You know that as well as I do."

The Governor turned her chair around and stared out at the lake below. When she turned back to her guests, Spivak spoke before she could reply. "My friends," he said, "a deal can't be concluded unless all sides are happy with the terms. If you're unhappy, then I'm unhappy, there's no deal and no defense alliance, and then the Prime Minister will be very unhappy. But there's another way to do it, Madam Governor. Instead of increasing the debt, you can raise the interest rate."

"I don't understand. Are you suggesting I interfere in the operation of the banks?" For the first time that morning, the Governor seemed confused.

"You're the Governor of the Central Bank. Simply announce you're raising the interest rate. Debts will become more costly. As a result, some people will decide to pay off their debts right away, and a slice of the pie will be freed up for our deal."

"But I don't set the interest rate."

"You don't?" This time it was Spivak who was confused. "So who does?"

"The banks," the Governor answered. "They get a

slice of the national debt and decide for themselves at what interest to offer it to their customers."

Once again, Spivak's hosts had refrained from mentioning a small, but very important, detail. The Governor didn't set the interest rate? How could that be? There were only two possibilities. Either it explained why the Central Bank occupied no more than a single office on the ninth floor that happened to have a sensational view and an impressive display of string instruments, or else the Governor wasn't being straight with him.

"I don't understand," Spivak said. "If you don't set the interest rate, then what do you do?"

"Me? I just watch over the pie. The national debt. My job is to prevent financial crises."

"I'm sorry," Spivak said, suppressing a laugh. "What do they say where I come from? It's all in the hands of the Governor. Why not be like other bank governors? They control growth, employment rates, stability, inflation. In fact, they direct all their country's economic activity just by adjusting the interest rate."

The Governor shook her head. "You can't convince me to upset the whole economy by changing the interest rate from nearly zero percent to two figures."

"You're exaggerating," Spivak exclaimed. "If you collect and analyze the data like you used to, you can fine tune the rate accordingly. When you sense the threat of inflation, you raise it, and when you see signs of a recession, you lower it to encourage consumption. You only have to change it by a quarter, or at most a half, a percent each time."

"A quarter of a percent is a non-change," the Governor said. "What difference will it make?"

"Not everyone is going to feel the difference right away. But if you owe half a million, it will reduce your monthly payment by two hundred. Two hundred and another two hundred spur consumption. If the economy is growing by 2.8 percent annually, that will push it up to 3.1 percent."

"Another three-tenths of a percent is a non-change," the Governor insisted. "If the economy is growing by 2.8 percent this year, it will grow by 3.1 percent next year or the year after. Of course, an increase of three-tenths of a percent is better than a decrease of three-tenths of a percent, but in both cases it's a non-change."

"Now you're going to say it's just a random fluctuation in the existing situation," Spivak replied, looking to the Finance Minister for help. "It's not three ounces of weight we put on after indulging in a dessert we shouldn't have eaten. Three-tenths of a percent represents billions in terms of economic activity."

"It may represent billions," the Governor said, "but fluctuations of fractions of a percent result from fluctuations in economic activity that at best are only marginally related to the actual state of the economy, and may even be totally arbitrary. They stem from short-term factors, like a temporary shortage of raw materials, the introduction of new models, sometimes even the weather." Addressing the Minister, she said, "You know as well as I do that the difference of a fraction of a percent in growth from one year to the next doesn't constitute a change. A rise doesn't indicate prosperity and a drop doesn't indicate a recession. They're no more than random fluctuations in the existing situation."

The Minister didn't reply. The longer he remained

silent the more it became clear to Spivak that he couldn't count on his help in his effort to move The Plan forward. Sighing, he turned back to the Governor. "In your opinion, three-tenths of a percent is a non-change. But when you report a decrease of three-tenths of a percent in growth, people reduce their spending for fear of a future loss of income, and companies freeze outlay and don't hire new workers. You may disregard it, but people respond and then there's a recession. Do you want to sit on your hands and wait for the next Big Crash? If you want to avoid it you have to listen to the little noises and quiet them by adjusting the interest rate."

"No, no, no. You're wrong," the Governor said emphatically. "When the Central Bank publishes figures that don't represent a change as if they did, it creates noise. And when you respond to noise, it gets louder." With a stern expression on her face, she went on. "In order to avoid a big crash you have to disregard the little noises. That's why we no longer collect or publish data."

Pushing her chair back, she stood up. She looked out at the lake gleaming like a mirror in the park below. Then she turned to face them. Quietly, she said, "The Central Bank doesn't need to encourage growth. That's not our job. The source of our wealth is the sunflower plant and other companies in the valley. A central bank that sees it as its job to promote the growth of the economy will keep lowering the interest rate, which will persuade people to increase their liabilities until eventually they won't be able to pay their debts. The bank will go from watching over the national debt to amplifying the noise. And so I will always see it as my sole responsibility to keep my eyes on the pie."

The room fell silent.

After a few tense moments, the Minister stood up. "It's not up to us. A war is coming, and we have to defend ourselves. If you don't want to change the interest rate, you'll have to let the pie grow. It's your choice."

"You won't get the solution you're looking for from me," the Governor said, the blood draining from her face. "Maybe it's time for you to use the purple sunflower. Wasn't it developed in order to protect the sunflower fields and the factories against the day when another country decides to invade and take them over?"

"Wherever we scatter the purple sunflowers, nothing will grow for forty years," the Minister said, lowering his eyes.

Chapter 11

The Driver's Show Business

It was almost lunchtime the next day. Spivak was still lying in his bed in the hotel room. A free day hadn't been on the schedule, but his host, the Finance Minister, had been summoned urgently to the Prime Minister. "I have to cancel all my appointments," he had informed Spivak, sounding very agitated. "I'll be with the Prime Minister all day." Spivak was disturbed by the thought of the imminent war, but he was mostly worried about its effect on the rising oil prices that were threatening to eat into his profits. He knew the trend had to be reversed, but the Governor of the Central Bank back home hadn't answered his calls for several days.

He turned on the television that occupied most of the opposite wall. The non-news, as they called it here, was only broadcast once a day, in the evening. He flipped through the channels, but nothing caught his interest. At home, everyone was still asleep. It was too early to try the Governor once more in an attempt to do something before the situation spun out of control. He switched channels again. Suddenly he was overcome by a sense of loneliness that only added to the uncertainty gnawing at him. He had to get out of the room.

On the path leading to the lake he saw the driver chatting under a tree with a man in a suit. He sat down on a bench. A few minutes later, she joined him.

"I see business is going well. I envy you," he said.

"I'm flattered that you find time to take an interest in my business despite all that's going on, both here and in your own country," she said, tightening her grip on her notebook.

"I have some free time," Spivak answered. "And it's clear to me that this bench is the perfect place to spend it." His eyes dropped to the notebook. "What isn't clear to me," he went on, "is what you're doing here instead of standing under a spotlight on stage. The last time we met you offered to take me to a show, but you didn't explain what kind of business you do here."

The driver looked around. They were alone. "The people you saw me talking to invest in the stock market. They buy and sell shares, and come to me to reduce the risk. That's what I do here."

Spivak reflected upon what he knew so far. In this world, the director of the stock exchange was basically a doorman who opened it up for an hour a day, industrialists gaped at you in wonder when you talked about trading their stock, the Governor of the Central Bank only watched over the debt and didn't set the interest rate, and sunflowers were purple. So, he reasoned, it shouldn't have surprised him when the aspiring actress he met who drove a car for a living was also a financial mediator. "If you're involved in risk management, why don't you work at the stock exchange?" he asked.

"Our stock exchange" the driver began, turning her eyes to the imposing building across the lake. "Well, you've been there. As I said, I improve the odds for the investors, but at the stock exchange they don't like what I do."

When Spivak didn't respond, she continued. "Take the sunflower stock, for instance. It's selling for ten today. They took you to the plant. You saw the latest developments in the greenhouse, right? I'm sure it's obvious to you that the price can easily rise to twelve next month. But if war breaks out, and we both know that's likely to happen, it could drop to eight. So anyone who buys the stock can make or lose two. That can cause a lot of stress. But there's a way to reduce the stress." She hesitated for a moment, then she handed Spivak her notebook.

"Here," she said. "Take a look at the first page. It's very simple. I could explain it with two hands on the steering wheel. Let's say I have a client who's holding sunflower stock and he's afraid there'll be a war and the price will go down. I find someone who believes the price will go up so he wants to buy it, but he doesn't want to risk the full amount of the purchase price in case he's wrong. So he agrees to pay my client one now in exchange for his commitment to sell him the stock next month at today's price. If war breaks out and the stock falls from ten to eight, the buyer won't want to purchase the stock from my client for ten. But he'll still have the right to back out of the deal, and he'll only lose the one he already gave him. My client also profits. The price of the sunflower stock went down by two, but he only lost one, because he got one last month for his promise to sell to the buyer. So because of the deal I brokered, they both lost less than they would have otherwise."

"Very nice!" Spivak exclaimed. "Where I come from, we call those stock options, the option to purchase a stock at an agreed-upon price at a specified time in the future. Where do you find the buyers who want to pay for the right to purchase stocks in the future?"

"Here in the park. They're also clients of mine. They believe the stock price will rise higher than the price they agreed on. Turn the page and you'll see how that works."

The rays of the afternoon sun shone on the lake. The swan flew over their heads and landed gently on the clear water, sending ripples outward that lapped at the stones along the bank.

Spivak closed the notebook and returned it to the driver. "Stock options make it possible for investors to share the risk. Everyone wins," he said. He noticed that his companion's attention was on the swan, who was swimming toward them. "But why do people come here to make a deal with you by a park bench?"

"Because that's the only way they can do it," she replied with no further explanation.

She poked around in her bag and brought out a packet of sunflower seeds. "Here's what I can do for you," she said, her eyes still focused on the swan. "When you got here, the Prime Minister and the Finance Minister assured us that everything would be fine now, so the investors are convinced that you'll take care of the problem and the price of the sunflower stock will rise. You don't have any sunflower shares, right? You don't need any. All you have to do is agree to sell the stock a month from now at the current price. By then, war will break out and the price will drop. No one will want to buy the stock from you at today's price because they can get it for less on the market. That will leave you with the money they already gave you." Getting up, she walked to the edge of the lake where she bent down and held her hand out to the swan. The bird paddled toward her and pecked the sunflower seeds from her palm.

When she had returned and sat back down beside him, Spivak said in a steely tone, "You realize that if there isn't a war, the stock price will rise. The investors will want to exercise their options, so I'll have to purchase shares for a higher price than we agreed on." Spivak rose. "You're setting me up for a huge loss, maybe even more than I can afford now," he said.

"Wait, don't go yet," she said, grabbing his arm. "They're telling everyone that nothing's going to happen, but we both know that war is inevitable. In the end they'll have to use the purple sunflower. At least you and I have a chance to profit from it."

Spivak gazed at the lake and the swan swimming contentedly in the water. He wiped his brow.

"You're asking me to bet against my own success."

"Nothing has come from any of the meetings you've had. You can see that yourself," she said. "I lost hope a long time ago. All I want now is to earn enough money to leave the country and devote myself to building an acting career somewhere else. They invited you here to negotiate an agreement that will get us a defense alliance, but by now you must realize that you can't do anything for us. Not with all the restrictions imposed by our system. They won't even allow you to make the sort of deal I'm offering you."

"Why? That's also forbidden here?" This country is full of surprises, he thought.

"Yes. There's this stupid regulation that says you can't agree to sell something you don't have. They call it a noise amplifier. Only someone who actually holds a stock can agree to sell it. It's been like that for forty years."

If she's right, Spivak thought, it's no wonder so many people came to meet with her in the park. He glanced at his watch. The people back home would be awake soon and he'd be able to try the Governor again. Maybe he'd finally take his call.

A plane passed overhead. The swan trembled, rose, and flapped its wings, its eyes fixed on them. When the engine noise faded into the distance, they heard the sound of violin music coming from across the lake. They were no longer alone. The driver stood up quickly and stuffed the blue notebook into her bag. "I have to go. If she's here, the meeting with the Prime Minister must be over and the Finance Minister will call for his car any minute. Think about what I said. The deal I'm offering is your only chance to get something out of your visit here."

Chapter 12

The Race For Barrels

On the table in his hotel room, Spivak's phone vibrated. A familiar name showed on the screen. "Finally," he grumbled to himself.

"Tell me, do I look like an idiot?" the Governor of the Central Bank at home thundered. "You get all excited about some pink sunflower they showed in you in some hole in the wall, and now it turns out that the only thing that's going to come out of that hole is a war. Why didn't you tell me? The market is going crazy. Did you happen to notice that?"

"I've been trying to reach you," Spivak said, his teeth clenched. "With oil prices what they are now, you can imagine I'm a little more concerned than you are. I'm the one who's about to go bankrupt any minute, not the country."

"Listen, I'm not kidding," came the voice from overseas. "The price is going through the roof. I know it's late where you are, but I need an answer before the end of the day. Run the figures and let me know: when are we going to start feeling the shortage here?"

Spivak could hear the hawk screeching on the other end of the line. For years it had been agitated by every unusual noise issuing from the capital market. But he didn't need any more indications of his old friend's mood. "I don't have to run any figures," he answered. "There's no oil shortage. Can't you shut that bird up?! The only thing that got me into this mess is you and your damned press conference."

"I spoke to you first," the Governor said defensively.

"If you'd told them about the sunflowers they grow here, it would have made headlines. It would have reassured the traders and the price of oil wouldn't have gone up. But you decided to leave that part out, and look what happened. What did you expect?"

"So what do we do now?" the Governor asked, his voice cracking. "Get me some real data. Your hosts must have research on alternative energy. Send me something convincing and I'll make sure it reaches the press. When the traders see it, they'll realize oil prices might go down."

"I don't think they do that sort of research. Anyway, this isn't a good time to ask them. Everyone here is preoccupied by more pressing issues. And I'm spending hours on the phone trying to get the banks off my back," Spivak said, glancing again at the stock ticker moving across his computer screen.

"We all know what the pressing issues are there, but I'm not sure you understand how pressing the issues are here," the Governor said. "Come on, give me something I can put out there that will douse the fire in the market. If oil prices keep going up, we'll be on the fast track to a recession. Send me whatever you can find."

The figures flashing on the screen in front of Spivak were all green. The graphs were showing a rapid rise and the hawk's screeching was getting louder. "It's too late," Spivak said. He pictured the bird on the Governor's right shoulder nervously flapping its wings as it did whenever trouble was brewing. "Nothing you give the press now will change the mood in the market. I don't think you have any choice. You have to put your money on the table."

"There's enough money in the central bank's pocket for whatever we need to do. Maybe you can find someone we can buy oil from on the sly? Within two days I can flood the market and bring the prices down."

"Do you really think any of the major oil producers will help you lower the price of oil? If I knew someone like that, I would already have bought a few barrels from him myself. My companies can't exist without oil. It won't be long before they collapse, and take me down with them. But you don't need oil," Spivak said, almost spitting the words. "As usual, when you panic you don't think straight. The problem isn't a shortage of oil. The problem is that people can't meet their commitments. The price of oil is rising because they transacted to sell barrels of oil they don't actually have. The shortage is just imaginary. If the central bank promises to sell them barrels in the future, the price will hold steady."

"I have no intention of bailing out those speculators. If you don't have any sellers for me, the country has emergency reserves. We can use them to flood the market," said the Governor.

"It's not enough. For every available barrel of oil, there are at least a dozen traders who sold empty promises to buyers, and now they're in a race to find every real barrel of oil they can," Spivak said.

"So what?" the Governor replied.

"You can see for yourself what's happening. The slightest rise in oil prices increases their losses, so they're looking all over for someone to buy barrels from before the price gets higher and they lose even more," Spivak said.

"They'll find someone in the end, but they'll take a loss on the difference between the price they committed to sell it and the current market price they need to buy it to fulfil their obligation," the Governor mumbled.

"How high do you want the price to go?" Spivak asked, wiping the beads of sweat from his brow. "It's their problem now, and mine, but before long it will be yours too. The higher the price goes, the more the traders will compete for every barrel in order to cap their losses. If you sit by and do nothing, the price will just keep going up. There'll be a bloodbath. You don't want a recession, do you?"

"So what do you suggest?" the Governor asked.

"I already told you. You have to put a stop to the panic as soon as possible. Every trader you promise to sell oil to at the current price is one fewer contender in the race for the barrels that are raising the price. By bailing out the speculators you're looking out for the economy. Trust me, you'll be the fair-haired boy of every politician in the country."

"I'll also be bailing you out. I'd be happy to do that," the Governor assured him, "but if the central bank commits to selling oil it doesn't have and some war that you forgot to mention breaks out, oil prices will go even higher. That will mean huge losses for the bank, and I can't allow that. Call me if you have any good news."

Spivak shut down his computer. There was no point in staring at the discouraging figures from the market floor. He had to find a way to save himself. He pulled out the business card the driver had given him, deliberating. If they didn't quote non-changes in stock prices at home, and if the traders were forbidden to agree to sell what they didn't have, the disastrous race for oil barrels that was playing out now wouldn't be possible. There wouldn't be a race for barrels, and he wouldn't find himself in a hotel room in a foreign country in the middle of the night considering a deal with a driver who sold questionable options by a lake with a swan. He was beginning to think there might be a good reason for the odd regulations the Governor and Finance Minister refused to budge from.

He slid back the glass door and stepped onto the balcony. He needed air. The cool breeze brought with it the sounds of violin music coming from the park. I can't fail here, he thought. By saving this country I'll also save myself. He gazed at the business card again. Returning to the room, he tore the small card into pieces and threw them in the trash.

Chapter 13

Practicing In The Park

Spivak left the hotel and walked rapidly toward the lake. He had to prevent a war. Now he could clearly hear the music of the violin. Another plane passed overhead, the noise startling a flock of birds who flew off, leaving behind a single swan swimming in the lake.

He stopped a few steps behind the violinist standing at the edge of the water and listened.

The piece she was playing came to an end and he clapped. "I see you're not worried, unlike everyone else, " he said to the Governor.

"By the same token, you could conclude that I went out to practice in order to calm my nerves," she said, picking up her instrument again.

"You could have helped," Spivak said, raising his voice to make himself heard over the music. "At the very least, I think I deserve an explanation. Why did you do everything you could to sabotage The Plan? The enemy is about to attack and you're here playing your violin. Maybe you can rethink your position."

She moved her bow back and forth in increasingly short strokes, and then suddenly raised it in the air. "You've been here long enough. I doubt you need any more explanations."

"I understand the situation. But it would all be so much simpler if you agreed to cooperate and do what we asked."

She didn't respond, but her playing grew less aggressive.

Eventually, she turned to face him. She lay down her bow and cleared the leaves off a nearby stone before sitting down, resting the violin and bow in her lap. Spivak stood behind her.

"If you can find anyone who loves this country more than I do, let me know," she said quietly, her eyes focused on the dark lake.

Another plane flew by. To Spivak it sounded even louder than the previous one, but the swan didn't appear to be frightened by the noise. It swam into the shallow water near them.

Once the plane was gone, Spivak sat down beside the Governor. "How much longer are you going to hide away in a lonely office with string instruments on the wall? If you go along with my proposal, you return to the big building opposite the stock exchange and you call the shots. Like all the leading bank governors."

"Haven't you figured it out yet? Your leading bank governors are trying to solve problems we haven't had for forty years," she said, making no effort to conceal the sarcasm in her voice.

"Your achievements are very impressive," Spivak answered. "But everyone knows that times have changed, and you have to do what you have to do. You can stick to your position on the debt pie and who should set the interest rates, but a war is coming and they're going to use the purple sunflower."

The Governor didn't budge. "You're the one who's talking about keeping the noise going and making us live with it too. You rejected the proposal that would have solved our problem and saved you the problems you're having today," she said, rising. "That was before you understood the principles of quiet. You could have prevented the war the moment you got here. You could have bought the sunflower company and joined hands with us."

Spivak glanced at his watch. It was almost midnight.

"It's not too late," the Governor said. "My van is waiting on the other side of the lake. Go."

Chapter 14

A Midnight Meeting

The Governor's driver took Spivak to the edge of the city. They passed through a gate and then followed a winding driveway to the entrance of a large estate.

A footman escorted him to a room where the Finance Minister and the Prime Minister were waiting. "I was hoping to meet with you under different circumstances," Spivak said, shaking their hands. "But time is running out for all of us."

"There's no need to apologize, Dr. Spivak," the Prime Minister said as they took their seats. "When there are urgent matters to discuss, any time is appropriate."

"So I'll get straight to the point. We have to go back to the original plan," Spivak declared. "You need a defense alliance, and I need the sunflowers because the price of oil is rising. If I buy the sunflower company and get you the military assistance you brought me here to broker, we can prevent the war, right?"

The Prime Minister looked over at the Finance Minister. Seeing the skeptical look on his face, Spivak hastened to add, "I give you my word I will regard the sunflowers as an investment. They will not be listed on our stock exchange."

"You'll have to invest all your capital," said the Finance Minister.

"All my capital?" Spivak asked. "Why?"

"That's how we do it here. All your capital, or at least the better part of it."

"I don't see why that's necessary," Spivak said, forcing a smile. The Finance Minister didn't respond. His face remained expressionless. Spivak realized that this last-ditch effort of his was about to hit another roadblock. The driver was right, he thought. It's impossible to do business with these people. His whole body broke out in a cold sweat. It was over.

"Gentlemen, we don't have time to argue over it now," the Prime Minister said, breaking the silence that had descended on the room. Turning to the Finance Minister, he instructed, "This is a state of emergency. Sell Dr. Spivak the sunflowers on whatever terms he wants. Otherwise we'll have to use the purple sunflower. We don't have any other options."

Chapter 15

The Curtain Goes Up

Spivak reached for the bowl of nuts on the table in his hotel room. A bottle of vintage champagne had been waiting in the minibar since his arrival, but it had never seemed the right time to open it before. He filled the ice bucket and got out the bottle. He would be leaving tomorrow, after addressing parliament. Luckily, his visit here wouldn't end in failure. But it had come very close.

The sound of the popping cork was joined by insistent knocking on the door. He opened it and the driver burst into the room. Perfect timing, he thought. He got another champagne flute from the cabinet and filled the two glasses. He held one out to her. "I'm glad you came," he said with a tired smile. "It's always better not to drink alone." But then he took in her disheveled hair and flashing eyes and realized that, once again, something more urgent was going to ruin his plans.

"It doesn't make sense, it just doesn't make sense," she muttered. Spivak placed the glasses on the table and led her gently to the sofa. "Sit down," he said. "What's wrong?"

She fell onto the sofa. "I just drove the Finance Minister home from your meeting," she said. "I had to fight back the tears the whole way."

"What happened?" Spivak asked.

"Prices were certain to drop. The enemy moving toward the border, getting ready to shell the fields, the Governor unwilling to raise the interest rate, the Finance Minister refusing to list the sunflowers on your exchange. You weren't making any progress."

"Oh dear. You bet on a drop in the price of the sunflower stock?"

"Yes. I was convinced it was a sure thing. War would break out, the stock price would plummet, and I'd keep the money the traders had given me." By now the tears were running down her cheeks. "But when you announce the defense alliance tomorrow, it will be the end of me. If the stock doesn't go down, how am I supposed to fulfill my commitment to sell it for a lower price?"

"Hold on a minute. How many options did you sell in total?"

"Each of the transactions was small, but all together I traded hundreds of options. Almost every investor wanted in," she said sobbing. "You saw them in the park. And now we'll have an alliance with your country and there won't be a war."

"You don't actually hold any sunflower stock?"

She shook her head, the tears continuing to stream down her cheeks.

Chapter 16

The Greyhound's Only Egg

A tall, pale man entered the restaurant by the lake and looked around. He caught sight of Spivak's wave, and made his way to the table. He greeted Spivak with a grunt, then sat and studied the lunch menu.

Spivak remembered first meeting the major investor on his visit to the sunflower plant. "Try to make friends with him this time. It might make it easier for him," the Finance Minister had said sourly as they were leaving the Prime Minister's house after concluding their deal. The man didn't raise his eyes until the waitress arrived at their table, smiling, but even then he didn't look directly at her. "Just coffee," he said shortly, handing her the menu.

"I could extend my visit and look into other investments you manage," Spivak said, in an attempt to start a conversation. Finally, the man looked up at him. "I don't manage investments, Dr. Spivak, I manage an investment. I put all the money investors give me in a single company which I keep a close eye on, as you saw."

"The company must be pleased," Spivak replied, "but why do the investors agree? Don't they want to put their eggs in a lot of baskets?"

"Our investors have a lot of eggs in a lot of baskets, but each investment manager only sits on one egg. In my case it's the sunflower company. That way we protect our citizens' investments and earn them the highest profit."

"I also try to earn the highest profit I can for my investors," Spivak said. "We're in the same business."

"Not at all," his companion said. "You try to earn more by choosing winners and losers."

"Of course, I try to beat the market return. That's how you make money in the stock market."

"Who makes money? A bad stock you take out of one portfolio becomes a bad stock in another portfolio. Buying and selling among investment companies improves the earnings of one citizen at the expense of the retirement fund of another."

"That's true. But if you place your money with the investment manager who earns the greatest profit, you come out ahead of the game."

"Are you sure?" the thin man said with a bitter smile. "What if your pension fund is in the hands of the manager who earned the most profit, but the money you saved to put your daughter through college is in the hands of one who recorded a loss? When investment companies compete against each other, the sum total of all the investors' capital doesn't change."

Spivak sighed. "I am already sold on the perils of overtrading, but maybe you can explain to me exactly what you do," he said.

"I told you. I sit on the egg. I represent the

stockholders on the board of directors, make sure they don't lose money."

"But why only one egg?"

"Tell me, Dr. Spivak," the Investment Manager said in a raised voice, "have you ever sat on the board of directors of a company that lost money?"

"Of course. Some of the companies I've invested in have reported losses, even big ones."

The noise around them had ceased for a moment. The restaurant began to clear the lunch service. The Investment Manager took a sip of the coffee that had been sitting in front of him for some time. Lowering his voice, he said, "What do you do when management makes a risky decision that is likely to cut into their profits?"

"I take my money out immediately," Spivak said with a smile. "You have nothing to worry about. I've got a good nose. It's saved me more than once."

"And what do the other investment managers on the board of directors do when they identify a risky move in a company you all hold stock in?"

"Everyone tries to protect their investments. Those who are quick enough take their money out of a losing company, and those who aren't sit and wait for their next opportunity. Nobody wants to hold stock in a sinking ship."

The Investment Manager glanced around at the other diners. "The ship isn't sinking, Dr. Spivak," he said, in a near whisper. "It's a ghost ship." He paused before adding, "It's only natural. Pardon the mixed metaphor, but if everyone has other eggs, no one is at the wheel. It's not worth it to anyone to steer the ship. But like me, each of our investment managers has only one egg to hatch, so we can't simply write it off."

"The sunflower company isn't just another egg, it's a golden egg," Spivak said, grinning. "You're very lucky."

"It's not luck, it's money. I undertook to invest most of my capital in the company, so I became the major shareholder, which meant I also became the manager of the fund that holds the sum total of shares in it. That arrangement is best for the investors."

"It was a very brave move on your part," Spivak said.

"The truth is, I didn't have any choice." The Investment Manager's eyes lit up as he looked directly at Spivak. "I thought the Prime Minister and the Finance Minister explained it all to you. For the past forty years, investment managers have had to agree to risk the lion's share of their capital."

Spivak remained silent. He hadn't realized how far the Prime Minister had gone in agreeing to sacrifice this principle in order to implement their rescue plan. "I would never dream of investing all my capital in one company," he said, although even he wasn't sure whether he was talking to himself or to his companion.

"I know," the Investment Manager replied." Where you come from, everyone wants to play the stock market, to manage diversified portfolios, to sit on a lot of boards of directors and go back and forth among them. But here you have to put all your money in one company in order to ensure your loyalty to the investment and the other shareholders. To ensure that you don't just look out for yourself."

Spivak was silent.

"I don't have any choice now," the Investment Manager said sorrowfully. "It's clear to me that you're not investing all your capital in the sunflower company, but I have to sell it to you anyway. We're in an emergency situation."

The sun was getting low in the sky. The Investment Manager leaned back in his chair and loosened his tie.

"This is the signed document," Spivak said, taking out the contract for his purchase of the sunflower company. "Trust me, it's a good deal. And most importantly, it's the only way to broker a defense alliance for your country."

"I understand that the Prime Minister and the Finance Minister see this sale as a way to save the country. Unfortunately, under these terms it won't save my investors."

The Investment Manager sighed heavily, his eyes fixed on Spivak. It was getting late and they were wasting time. The restaurant had emptied out. They stared at each other in silence.

Spivak tried to think of a way to move things along. He thought of the large investment he'd made before coming here, and how he'd almost lost it all when oil prices went through the roof, thanks to the speculators. He thought of his home country, where savings and investments went into trading that brought no benefit to the national economy and only led to one crisis after another. Then he thought of his old friend, the Governor of the Central Bank, who hadn't been able to rescue him this time. It occurred to him that he himself was part of the problem. Glancing out the window, he noticed golden hour's warm, cozy light. Then he caught sight of a brown bird with a short beak hopping on a rock at the edge of the lake. The swan swam calmly toward it. Spivak smiled to himself. If the Governor at home let his lucky hawk out, he would also enjoy the quiet. He took a deep breath, crossed out the clauses in the contract that had been added especially for him, and turned the document around to face the Investment Manager. "I assume this will satisfy you," he said.

Chapter 17

Check-Out

Spivak pushed aside the breakfast tray and looked out through the large window of his room. The lush greenery in the park shone in the bright sunlight. Fleecy white clouds drifted across the blue sky and the lake was as smooth as a mirror. His eyes wandered to the empty bench. The driver wouldn't be coming any more. A few minutes later he gathered up the papers on which he had outlined the main points of his speech and slid them into the pocket of his jacket. Grabbing the handle of his suitcase, he left the room.

By now he was used to seeing the lobby occupied mainly by military personnel of various ranks, but this morning it was filled with men in light suits and women in summery dresses. At the far side, the Finance Minister and the Governor sat with their eyes fixed on the elevator he had just exited. They waved, gesturing for him to join them. He walked toward them, leaving his suitcase with the bellboy.

"My van will be here any minute," the Finance Minister said crisply. He looked quite a bit younger than the last time Spivak had seen him. He sat down beside them. "We have time for a cup of coffee," the Minister said, beckoning to a waitress who hurried over.

"It's good to see you again," the Governor said, looking very much like the smiling woman he had first met by the lake. "Thanks to you, Dr. Spivak, today's festivities will be especially joyful."

"It's a great honor for me to address parliament on the occasion of your fortieth year. I prepared a speech before I came, but I rewrote it last night," he added with an impish grin.

"Even at the most difficult moments, I always believed we'd get there in the end," declared the Finance Minister.

"I'm glad you stood your ground," Spivak replied.

"Thank you for agreeing to our terms," the Minister went on. "It was very generous of you." As he gestured for the bellboy, the Governor leaned over to Spivak and whispered, "The driver was fired this morning. I'm sure you understand we didn't have any choice." The bellboy confirmed that the Finance Minister's van was waiting outside.

An unfamiliar driver opened the van door. The Governor got in first, with Spivak and the Finance Minister right behind. As they took off, Spivak turned to his companions. "Can't you give her a second chance?" he said. "Gambling can be very seductive. At least your speculators did their gambling in the park and not in the Central Bank."

Chapter 18

The Speech

"When times change, we have no choice. We have to change too.

"You invited me to visit your country after years of self-isolation.

"I came to strengthen the ties between our countries and broker a defense alliance that will help protect you from a covetous enemy preparing to attack.

"We have formulated a plan.

"Alliances between countries are based on mutual interests deriving from the assets each side brings to the table. Your yellow and pink sunflowers are a marvel, not to mention the purple flowers. But your greatest asset is a little secret that is very powerful and which the world has yet to learn.

"Your secret is locked up in the stock exchange, whose chairman is also the doorman who opens its doors for an hour a day and does not quote small changes in stock prices.

"Your secret is also hidden away in an economy overseen by a part-time bank governor who does not collect financial data and does not adjust the interest rate, but merely ensures that the national debt does not grow larger.

"Your secret is guarded by a finance minister who knows that maintaining quiet is the best way to maintain prosperity.

"The time has come for the the world to address the noise factor and switch off the three noise amplifiers.

"The first noise amplifier is the quoting of small random fluctuations in stock prices. Although such fluctuations do not indicate real change, traders respond to them. The response increases activity in the market and changes the price of the stock regardless of the actual state of the company, thus deceiving investors.

"As a visitor to your country, I have learned that all it takes is a single regulation to preserve the connection between the stock price and the state of the company: non-changes cannot be quoted.

"The second noise amplifier is stock options. Considered a way to manage risk, they have turned into a high stakes betting game. Small fluctuations in the value of assets become large fluctuations of profit and loss in the options on the assets. The effect of these changes is felt in the prices of products, which rise and fall sharply and rapidly without any regard for actual demand, thus deceiving consumers.

"As a visitor to your country, I have learned that all it takes is a single regulation to preserve the connection between the demand for a product and its price: no one can commit to selling what they don't have. This will prevent the kind of race that raises prices for no reason.

"The third noise amplifier is a central bank that

governs economic activity by adjusting the interest rate, collecting financial data about random fluctuations that do not represent change and responding by progressively lowering the interest rate. The bank thereby encourages consumption by increasing the debt, which grows larger and larger until the bubble bursts, generating a major economic crisis that leads to unemployment and recession.

"As a visitor to your country, I have learned that consumption fueled by debt is a cheap fertilizer that promotes only temporary growth and prosperity, and that the central bank has one function alone: to diligently preserve a stable ratio between the national debt and the gross domestic product. That is sufficient to prevent the next crash.

"I am a visitor to your country, but I am no longer a stranger here.

"I have purchased the sunflower company, and as of yesterday, it is the only egg in my basket.

"I have made enough noise for now. From this day forward, it will be my mission to spread your secret of quiet."

☼ The End ☼

Epilogue

First interview with Dr. Spivak

If noise is just noise, why should we care about it?

The common view in economics is that noise is not something to worry about. If you ask an economist what the impact of noise is on the stock market, the common answer would be: "Not much." If you keep nagging, they will explain that the stock prices tend to have random fluctuations. But these fluctuations dissipate in the process, so eventually the stock prices reflect the underlying value of the business.

According to this perception, the more we trade, the better the market will process new pieces of data and sift out the irrelevant part—the noise. In addition, since the noise is random, traders cannot use these fluctuations to generate consistent profit from their trades. They cannot beat the market average return. If the noise is sifted out of the system, and in the process no one can expect to make an excessive return, then the noise has no effect on the stock market.

The problem with this perception is that it ignores a fundamental truth: when we react to noise, the noise level increases. Noise doesn't dissipate when we react to it.

How does the reaction to noise increase the noise level?

The best way to answer this question is to look at a different field outside economics where the importance of noise is deeply understood. From the early days of mass production, industrial engineers had to deal with product quality issues and reduce variations in the manufacturing process. They soon realized that trying to eliminate some variations increases the overall level of variation. Some variations result from a fault in the process—and that fault needs to be fixed—while other variations are just normal fluctuations (noise). When we react to those normal variations by adjusting the production process, we increase the overall variation.

I assume you are referring to the work of William E. Deming?

Yes, Deming was one of the thought leaders in management and quality. His famous funnel experiment is a good way to demonstrate what happens when we react to noise.

In the experiment, a marble is dropped through a funnel onto a sheet of paper on which a target is drawn. The goal is to get the marble to hit this target.

During the first setup, the funnel is aligned above the target, and marbles are dropped from this location. The results are always disappointing. The marbles do not behave consistently; they roll off in various directions for various distances. When we record each performance of the experiment, we get something like this graph:

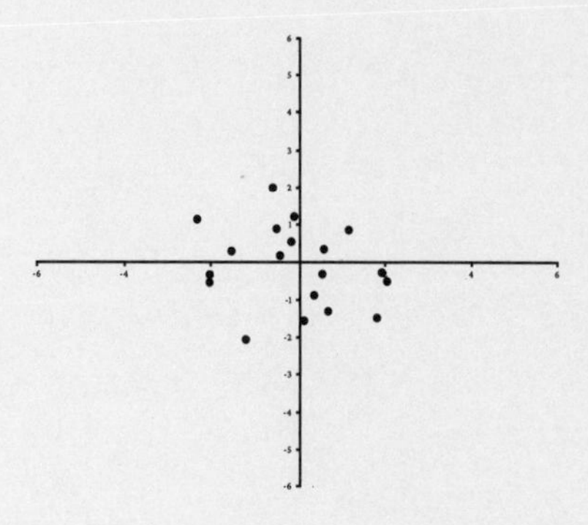

Now let's see what happens when we try to improve performance. We will repeat the experiment, but this time we will change the position of the funnel based on the results we get. After each drop, we will adjust the funnel in the opposite direction from the target to compensate for the last error. If, for example, the marble rolled two inches northeast last time, we should set the funnel two inches southwest of the target. Then when the marble again rolls two inches northeast, it will hopefully stop on the target. When we play this game for a few iterations we get a very different result:

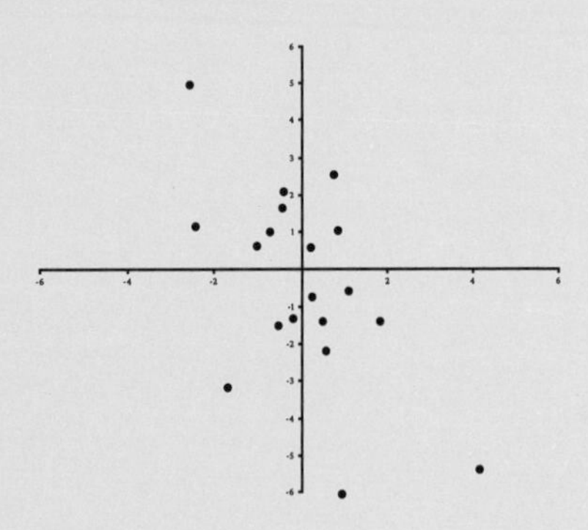

What we see is that the counter-reaction increases the degree of variability. The results swing back and forth with greater and greater oscillations from the target, creating an unstable system.

How does this experiment relate to our economic system?

Counter-reaction is usually used when we try to maintain parity or equilibrium. Central banks use counter-reaction as a main strategy to keep the economy on a desired course. For example, if the number of new jobs is too small or new house construction is down, the Central Bank may try to stimulate the economy by lowering the interest rate. Every stimulation is a counter-reaction. The problem is that counter-reaction feedback creates greater oscillations and distortions in the system.

In his experiment, Deming presented other compensation mechanisms, all of which demonstrate the same point: when you react to noise, the noise level increases.

But if central banks do nothing, won't their economies fall into a recession?

The problem is not with the state of our economies. Our economies are resilient. They may fluctuate, but they don't need constant supervision and support to operate normally. The problem is with our perception. If we believe that the economy is fragile, it will be fragile. It is a self-fulfilling prophecy. We believe that the system is volatile and fragile so we counteract noise, which in return increases variability and cyclicality. Then we feel we have the "proof" that the system is fragile. Central banks should stop monitoring the public mood. Tracking public confidence or fear is just tracking noise. Central banks should act and stimulate the economy only in extreme—and rare—conditions.

Let's table the discussion on central banks for a moment. How can we avoid reacting to noise?
We need to filter out the noise from the signal. For example, in the funnel experiment we could draw a circle around the target. As long as the marble falls within that circle, we should not take any corrective action.

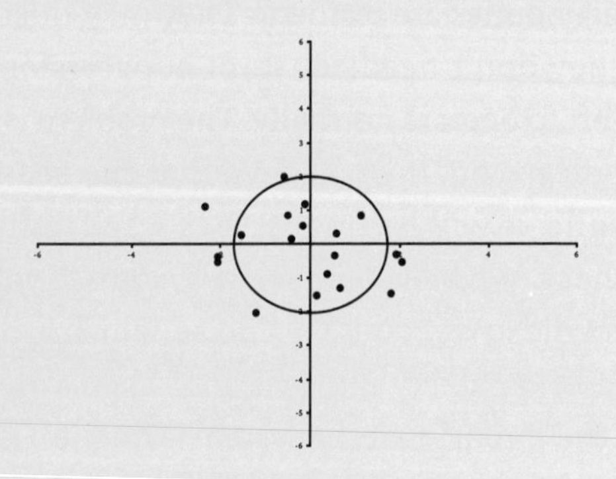

Industrial engineers use control charts, also known as Shewhart charts, to distinguish the "noise" within the target from the true deviation. The control chart is a statistical tool that monitors manufacturing or business processes to determine if the process is in control. The control chart has lower and upper bounds. As long as the fluctuations are between these two, individual variance can be ignored.

In electronics, engineers use a combination of capacitors and resistors to filter the noise. Our audio systems and phones all use capacitors to filter out the noise to produce a clear sound.

In economics, the first step in suppressing the noise is to make sure that the system doesn't record the noise.

What does this mean for our financial system?

Financial markets should not record small fluctuations in price. Once you record a small fluctuation, the "corrections" made in reaction to the fluctuation, just like in the marble experiment, will lead to bigger fluctuations.

We can argue all day about what a "small"

fluctuation is and where we should draw the line. Our guideline should be a simple principle: you can never be more accurate than the noise.

When we estimate the value of a given company, 5 percentage would definitely be within the margin of error. Trying to be more accurate than 5 percentage is definitely playing with noise. I put the line at 10 percentage. But any number between 5 percentage and 10 percentage will do. We can design our own capacitor.

You didn't stop there; you also advocate for minimizing trading hours! Why?
Immediate feedback to noise just amplifies noise. We all know that when the mic gets too close to a speaker, it makes a horrible squeaky sound.

If for most of the day there is no real signal, long trading hours are just a response to noise.

It seems that you ignore the impact on liquidity.
Liquidity is not the goal. Actually, we have too much liquidity.

Maximum liquidity is an objective for a system that focuses on short term trading gains and not on long term investments. You don't check the price of your house five times a day in the market. Why would you do it with other long-term investments? Too much liquidity breeds too little commitment.

This is a clear case of the tail wagging the dog. Essentially, shares gives the public access to investments in the best and largest companies. The ability to sell the shares easily within a day is a bonus to individuals. What may have started as side benefit has taken front stage.

You also advocate limiting the ability to sell stock options and other derivatives. What is the reason behind this suggestion?

The classical view is that derivatives contracts and stock options are tools that enable operators and investors to effectively share the risk and limit the risk to which they are exposed.

For example, let's say an airline sells tickets for summer vacation 4 months ahead of time. The ticket price assumes a given oil price. Fuel is a significant part of the flight cost. If, during that time, the oil price goes up, the airline may lose a lot of money. A futures contract between the oil producer and the airline to buy oil at a certain price Four months from now provides certainty for both.

I don't see the problem.

The problem is that most contracts are between people like you and me. I don't own an airline, and you don't own an oil field. We are just two speculators; each takes a different side of the bet.

Now, if it is just you and me, this is not a problem. But when you have many more speculators in each market than operators or investors, it becomes a severe problem. When you sell what you don't have, it is easy to create big artificial waves of supply and demand. These artificial spikes make prices more volatile. Again, this volatility is not a result of economic activity, just of sheer speculation.

We have learned the hard way to treat inflation as a hidden tax. Artificial volatility is just the same. It is a hidden tax on investors and operators. Both need to buy more protection to run their businesses and protect their investments.

We live through the following vicious cycle: the more derivative contracts we have, the more volatile the system and the higher the demand for insurance in the form of derivative contracts, and so on.

Derivative contracts are seductive because they turn small fluctuations—noise—into big profits and losses. If people want to speculate, they should play poker or bet on horse races, rather than be given access to our financial market where they mess things up.

Some people may argue that noise is just another excuse to get the government more involved in the markets. How would you address their concerns?

In economics we have a common analogy where we describe prices as the "traffic lights" of the economy. Just like traffic lights regulate traffic, prices regulate economic activity. Economists warn against government intervention that may distort prices which will then also distort economic activity.

When the noise level is high, it is harder to tell what is signal and what is noise, what is real and what is not. When the noise level increases, it is as if the traffic lights are giving us confusing signals. It has a big impact on public savings and on allocation of capital.

But how can you ensure that this will not be an excuse for excessive regulation and a tighter government grip on the market?

Unstable systems break, which brings much more government intervention. Each financial crisis brought more regulation and created more bailouts where the government chose winners and losers.

Regulation is often used as a "patch" on the weak spots within the financial system. For example, we use securitization to enable banks to lend much more with less capital. Then we try to protect against the risk of the bank reselling bad loans by introducing loads of regulation on the securitization process. Similarly, we enable traders to sell what they don't have, and then we try to protect against the risk of mass default with reams of counter-party risk regulation. Over time, from one crisis to another, the system oscillates between more regulation and then deregulation.

Regulation should not fix the flaws of the system. It should define a system with no serious flaws.

What would you do differently?

We first need to recognize that the rules of how the

financial markets operate are not laws of nature. They are a result of the choices we have made and continue to make.

We can have rules that increase noise and variability and make the system more profitable for traders. Or we can design the system so it will filter noise and unnecessary variability in a way that will create focus around its original idea: a marketplace for investors.

If we design the system to support a commitment to long term prosperity for everyone, it will be far simpler and require less regulation.

Back to your criticism on central banks. The governor is your friend. I am sure he is not happy when you call central banks the big noise amplifiers.
The status quo is not a result of bad intentions, but an outcome of chasing the wrong goals. It is too common for central banks to chase the goal of stronger economic growth and a higher employment rate. While these goals are noble, central banks have only remote and indirect effects on employment and economic activity by changing interest rates and promoting more debt.

The assumption is that more debt fuels more investments and consumption, which in turn creates more jobs. While this is partly true, the impact of this approach is temporary and small compared to other factors that directly impact the job market, such as new technology, access to relevant education, and international trade.

To counteract all other factors and stimulate the economy, central banks set interest rates lower and lower and promote more debt. But these actions cannot guarantee that the debt will finance new technology and not stock buybacks. Historical data does not suggest that these stimulations create a positive impact; in fact, it shows the opposite. Eventually the mounting debt increases the likelihood of a financial crisis. Every financial crisis brings a significant spike in unemployment, which is exactly the opposite of the maximum sustainable employment goal.

What should the right goal be for central banks?

Central banks, as their name implies, should focus solely on maintaining the stability of the financial system. It is in their power (and in fact it is their job!) to prevent financial crises, which is how they should contribute to sustainable growth.

It is relatively easy for a central bank to control the overall debt level and prevent financial crises. All they need to do is to demand enough equity against every loan. An equity requirement is a simple anchor to control debt expansion and prevent financial bubbles and debt crises. Whether it is an individual taking out a mortgage, companies that take out loans or issue debt, or the commercial banks themselves providing loans, they all need to be supported with enough equity as defined by the central bank.

Speaking of anchors, do you support a return to a gold standard? It would definitely eliminate fluctuations in the currency market.

No, I don't. Reacting to noise increases noise. But it is also important to remember that a very delayed reaction to a signal increases noise.

Think, for example, about a big building with an automated air-conditioning unit where the thermostat is located in a remote part of the building. The first signals to come in from the temperature sensor may report that the building is still too cold. The air conditioner may begin to dispense heat, and the building becomes too hot. So then the thermostat signals for cooling, but once again, it takes time to change the temperature, and the building becomes too cold. The fluctuation has to do not with the actual outside temperature, but with the lack of synchronization between the air conditioner and the measuring device. It is the nature of the delayed feedback mechanism that creates the oscillation.

The same thing may happen with the gold standard. For example, a country may endure a long international trade deficit while its currency maintains its value in gold. The fixed exchange rate hinders the country ability to reduce its trade deficit. Eventually, as the country's gold reserve dwindles, a sharp devaluation of the currency is unavoidable. Holding currencies fixed to a gold measure prevents necessary price adjustments. It forces artificial stability until the system eventually breaks.

Is the idea of delayed reaction to a signal just a theoretical concern? Where can we see it play out

in our economy?

Even without the gold standard, some central banks act within the currency market to maintain a desired exchange rate. The longer the bank artificially maintains an exchange rate, the higher the chance it will backfire. Chronic trade deficits can lead to political instability, protectionism, and trade wars.

Another example: when a central bank holds the interest rate close to zero for too long, it forces the economy into a cycle of expansion and contraction. The bank triggers a short-term increase in economic activity, which eventually results, due to an increase in debt and inflated asset prices, a long-term decay.

Delayed feedback in its extreme form happens when a central bank consistently increases the credit supply until it sees an increase in the default rates. This is an extreme example of waiting for a very late signal to course correct.

You advocate for a fundamental change in the role of the mutual fund industry. How is this industry related to noise?

In the narrow aspect of amplifying noise, there

is no connection. Mutual fund and other asset management entities are, by definition, long-term investors. In that context there is nothing wrong with the way they operate.

So why should they change?

Mutual funds and other asset managers are agents who manage the public's investments. As agents, they have two jobs: they choose investment portfolios and represent the public on the companies' boards. They currently compete on portfolio selection and represent the public on companies' boards as part of their fiduciary responsibility without any compensation. I think it should be the other way around. It would create an opportunity for the funds to deliver much more substantial value.

Are you back to the old argument that, over time, you can't beat the average market return?

This is not the point. An individual fund may or may not be able to consistently beat the market return. I would not spend time arguing about that. As a public we can't beat the market return; we own the whole market! By definition, the majority of funds cannot beat the average market return.

How can we do better?

Trying to choose winners and losers is a zero-sum game. It doesn't improve the overall market return. The job of portfolio selection provides no value to the public as a whole, and very little value for most individuals.

If you look at the stock index over time, you can see countless companies that fell badly from grace. What a lot of these companies have in common is that at some point they disregarded the perspective of a dominant shareholder who acted and thought like a founder.

What do you suggest?

Think about a world in which we pay our agents to act like founders. A world where there is a separation between the advisory service of portfolio selection and the act of managing investments. A market where in every public company there is at least one asset manager who is exclusively invested in the company and acts as the major shareholder. In this role, the asset manager can make sure the CEO focuses on creating value for the long term rather than managing the stock.

We do have private equity funds. How are they different?

The active role and the responsibilities of the funds are similar. The set-up is different. Private equity funds typically invest for a period of seven years and exit when the company goes public. I am talking about investing in a public company and representing the public for a longer period, something like Twenty years. The fund that takes on the commitment to the public company could represent all the small shareholders for a certain management fee.

How would a fund be elected for this role?

The fund would be elected based on its financial commitment to invest its founders' money in the public company. The competition between the funds is competition on commitment, not on marketing.

This is a radical change. How realistic is it to expect the industry to adopt it?

This proposal is the last stage of the change, not the first. The change should start with the central banks. Commercial banks love volatility. They prosper with noise. The higher the noise, the higher the margins on many of their financial products. You can't expect commercial banks to lead the change. Currently, central banks promote more debt, less equity, and an inflated derivative market. Central banks need to lead the change and turn off all the noise amplifiers.

Some may say you are suggesting a very boring future...

As an old philosopher said, "Noise distracts the mind." We may personally love the distraction that comes with noise—it can be exciting! But our addiction to noise damages economies, companies, and individuals. The question is, then: are we willing to pay the price of our addiction to noise?

Yishai Ashlag holds a Ph.D. in economics from Bar Ilan University. Upon graduation, he was a visiting scholar at the Wharton School of Business. Yishai is an entrepreneur and an expert in the Theory of Constraints. Currently, he is a senior partner at Goldratt Consulting. THE NOISE FACTOR is his fourth book.